Eric Clapton.

Blues Power.

Wise Publications
London/New York/Sydney

Exclusive Distributors:
Music Sales Limited
8/9 Frith Street,
London, W1V 5TZ, England
Music Sales Pty. Limited
120 Rothschild Avenue,
Rosebery, NSW 2018,
Australia

This book © Copyright 1991 by Wise Publications
Order No. AM83528
ISBN 0-7119-2534-8

Designed by Pearce Marchbank Studio
Compiled by Peter Evans
Front cover photo by Kristin Vraa/LFI
Back cover photo by Mike Guastella/Star File

Music Sales complete catalogue lists thousands of titles and is
free from your local music book shop, or direct from Music Sales Limited.
Please send a cheque/postal order for £1.50 for postage to
Music Sales Limited, 8/9 Frith Street, London W1V 5TZ

Printed in the United Kingdom by
JB Offset Printers (Marks Tey) Limited, Marks Tey, Essex.

Your Guarantee of Quality

As publishers, we strive to produce every book to the highest commercial standards.
All the music has been freshly engraved and the book has been carefully designed to minimise
awkward page turns and to make playing from it a real pleasure.
Particular care has been given to specifying acid-free, neutral-sized paper which has not been
elemental chlorine bleached but produced with special regard for the environment.
Throughout, the printing and binding have been planned to ensure a sturdy, attractive
publication which should give years of enjoyment.
If your copy fails to meet our high standards, please inform us and we will gladly replace it.

Tablature & Instructions Explained

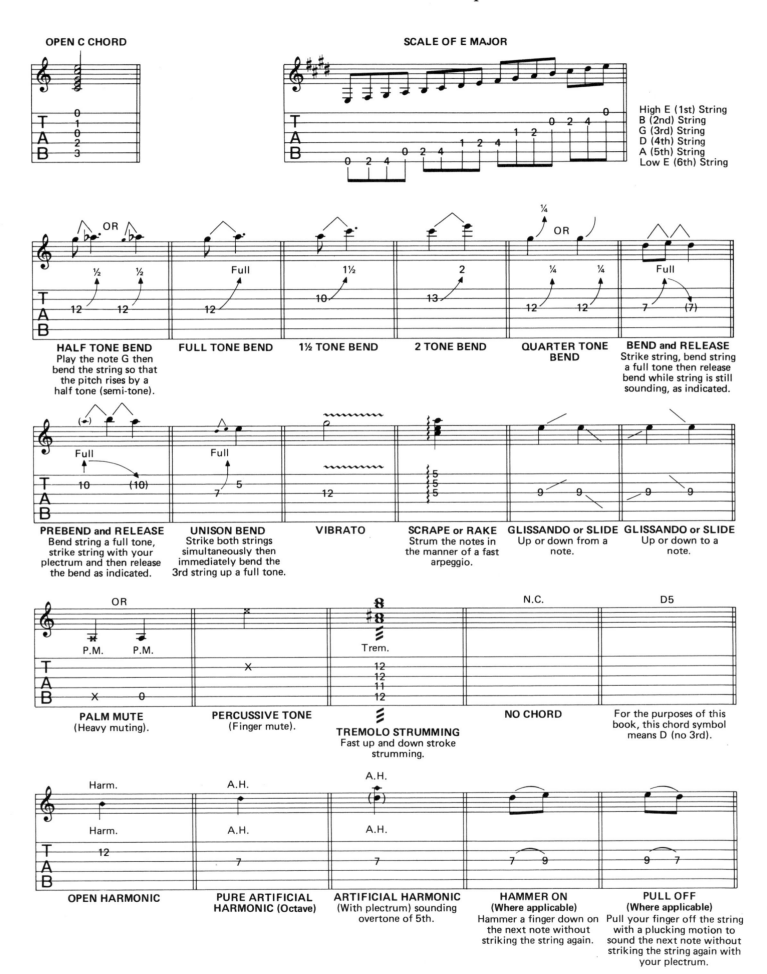

Blues Power.

Words & Music by Eric Clapton & Leon Russell.

Introduction

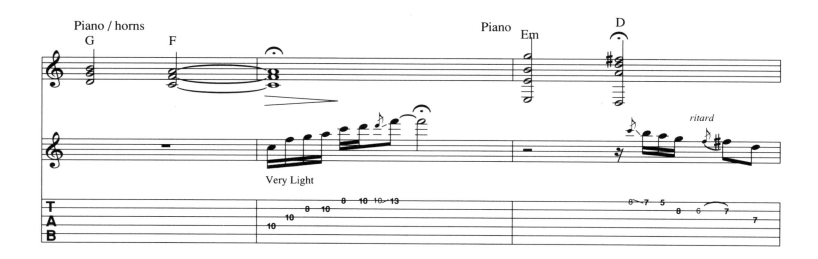

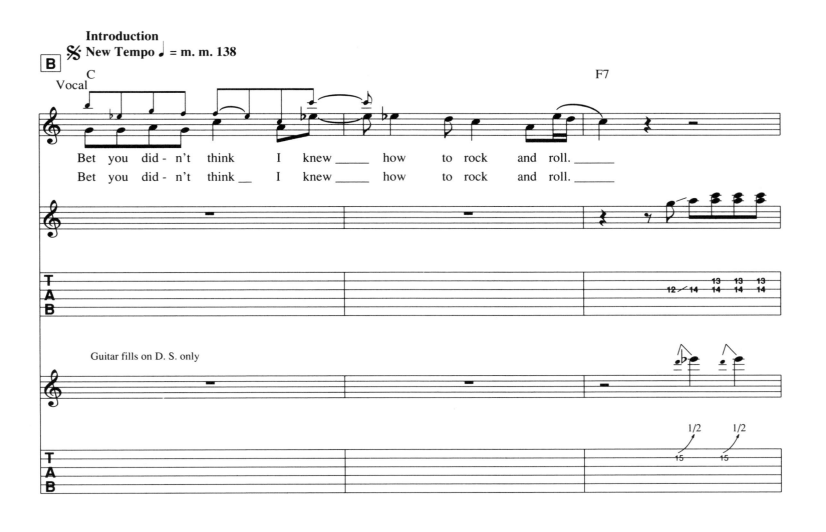

Introduction
New Tempo ♩ = m. m. 138

Bet you did - n't think I knew _____ how to rock and roll. _____
Bet you did - n't think __ I knew _____ how to rock and roll. _____

Guitar fills on D. S. only

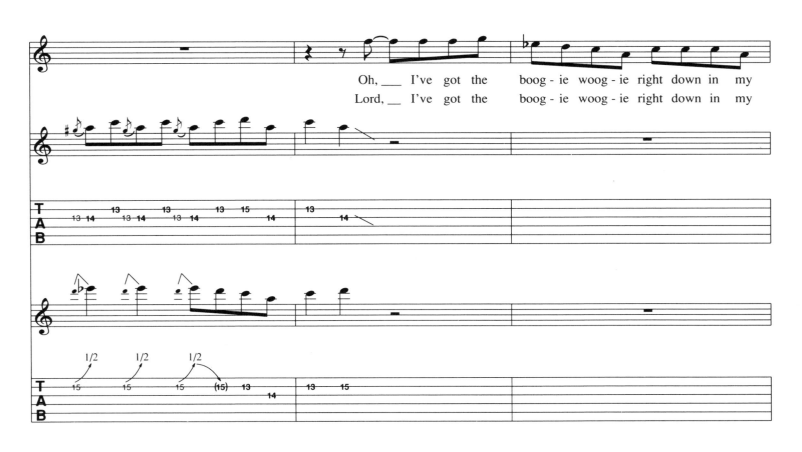

Oh, ___ I've got the boog - ie woog - ie right down in my
Lord, __ I've got the boog - ie woog - ie right down in my

ver - y soul. _____   There   ain't   no   need   for

ver - y soul. _____   There   ain't   no ____   need _

let ring

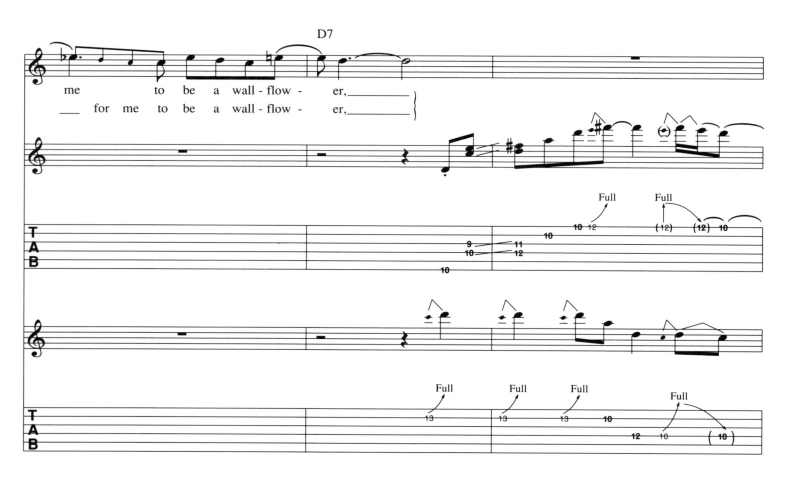

me   to   be   a   wall - flow -   er, _____

___ for me   to   be   a   wall - flow -   er, _____

now I'm gon - na let you know: ____

I'm gon - na keep on rock- in', no mat - ter if it's fast ___ or slow. _

Ain't gon - na stop _____ un - til the twen - ty - fifth hour, _

'cause now I'm liv- in' on blues __

Guitar Solo Interlude #2

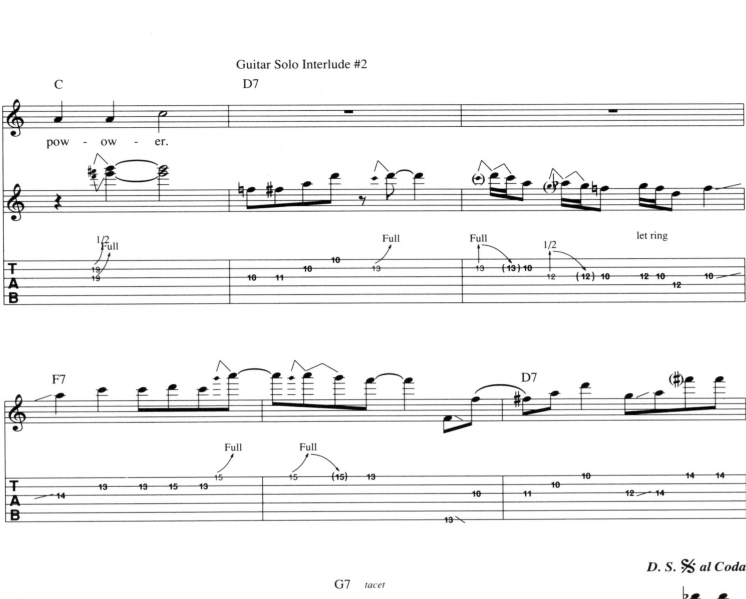

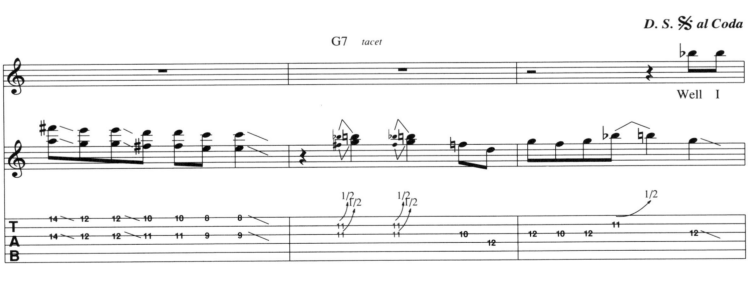

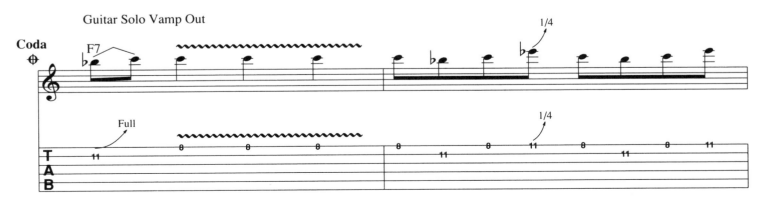

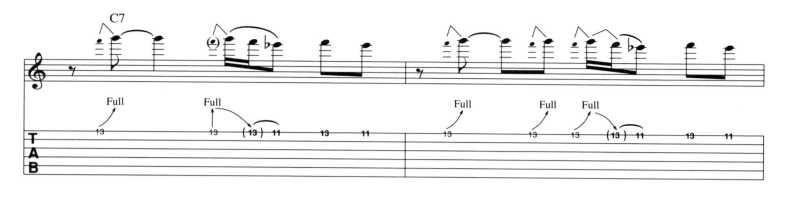

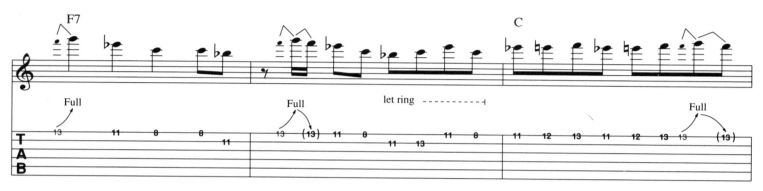

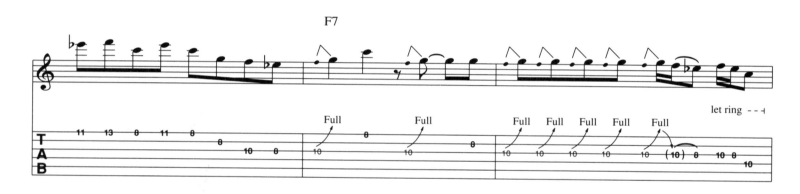

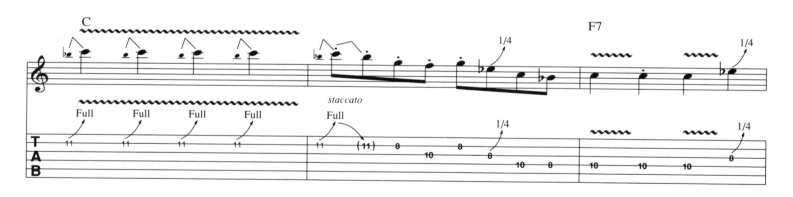

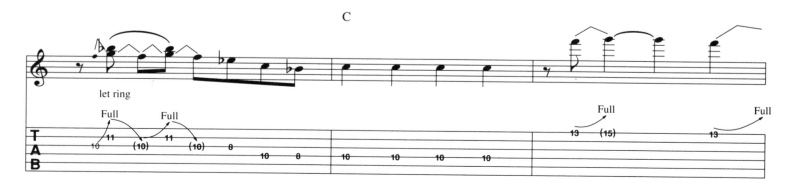

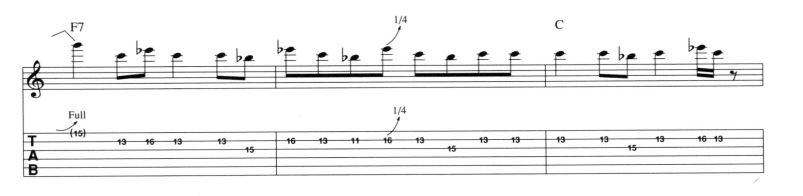

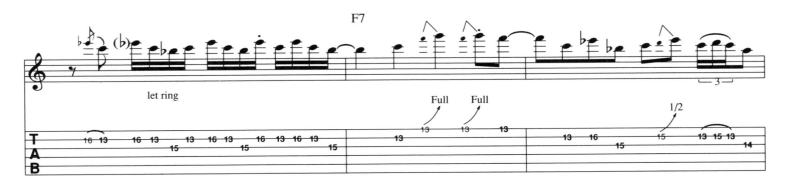

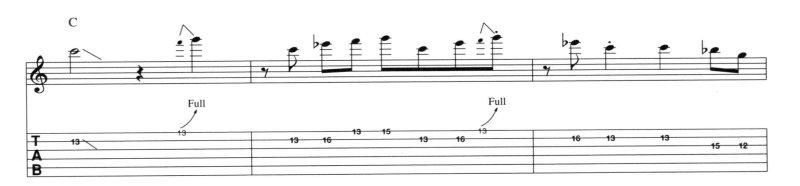

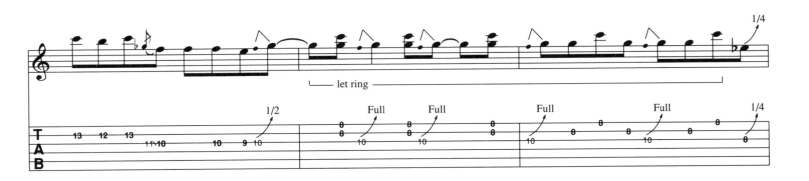

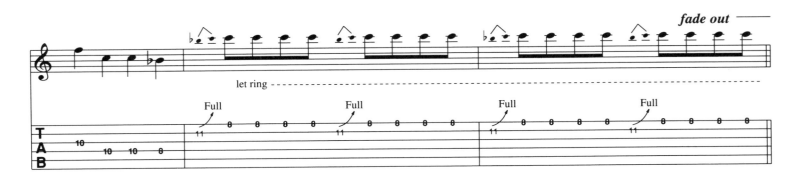

Better Make It Through Today.

Words & Music by Eric Clapton.

and if I can't make it through _ to - mor - row
when I look a- round _____ me

all __ I see __

I bet- ter make it through _ to- day. _
is mis - er - y. __

Electric
Guitar

to Coda ⊕

"Life is what you make it,"

at least that's __ what __ the peo- ple say; _____

and if we can't make it through to- mor - row ____

we

Electric guitar

15

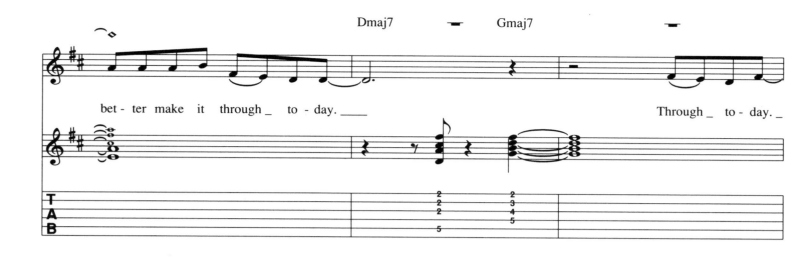

bet - ter make it through _ to - day. ____

Through _ to - day.

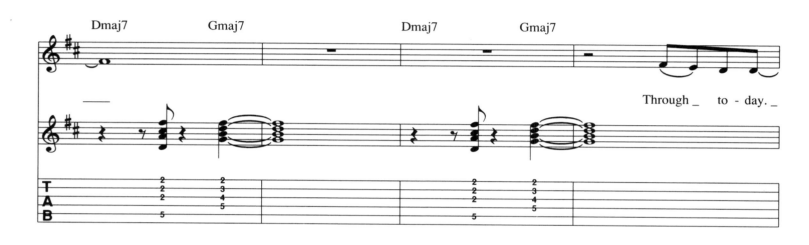

Through _ to - day. _

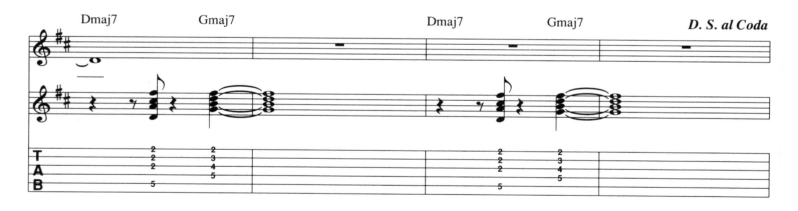

If I Don't Be There By Morning.

Words & Music by Bob Dylan & Helena Springs.

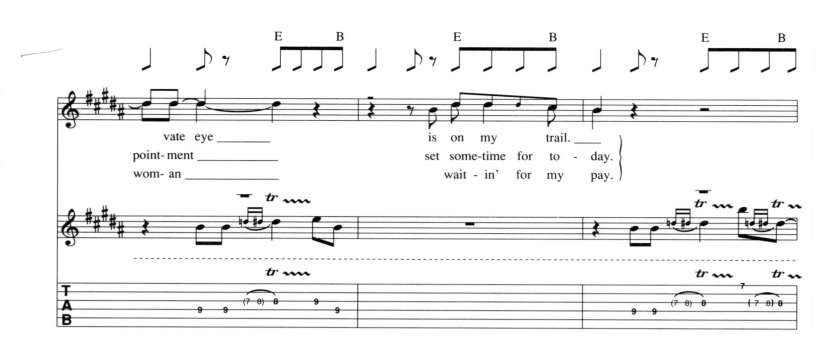

vate eye _____   is on my trail. _____
point-ment _____   set some-time for to - day.
wom- an _____   wait - in' for my pay.

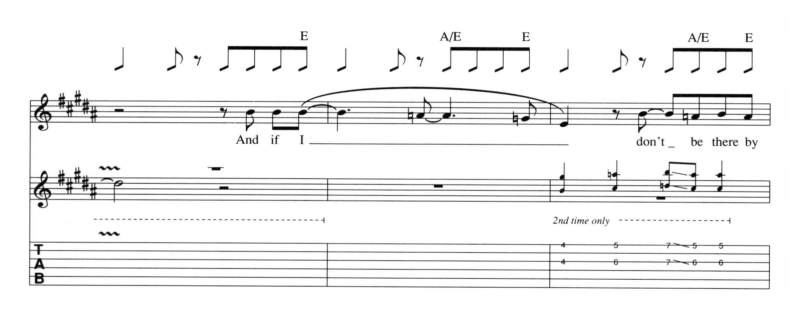

And if I _____ don't _ be there by

2nd time only

morn - ing, __   you know that I ____
you know that I ____
pack my clothes, ____

(tacet 2nd time only)   3rd time only

must have spent the night in _____ jail.
must have gone the oth-er _____ way.
get down on your knees and _____ pray.

I been run-

Find-ing my way back to you, ___ girl, lone-ly and blue ___

and mis-treat-ed, too. ___ Some-times I think of you, _

___ girl. Is it true ___ that you think _ of me too? ___

19

Key To The Highway.

Words & Music by Big Bill Broonzy & Chas. Segar.

billed out and bound to go. _____ I'm gon-na leave, __

billed _____ out and bound to go. I'm gon-na

yeah, I'm run-nin'; walk-in' is much _ too slow. __

leave here run-nin'; walk-in' is much _ too slow. _____

done noth - in',   drove a good   man ___ a - way   from

done noth - in',

home. __   *(1st time only)* As   the

to Coda ⊕

moon _____   peeks o - ver the   moun - tains, __

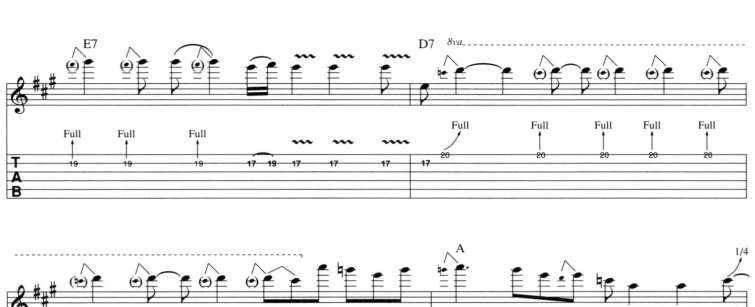

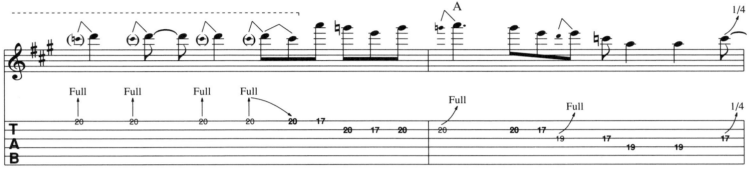

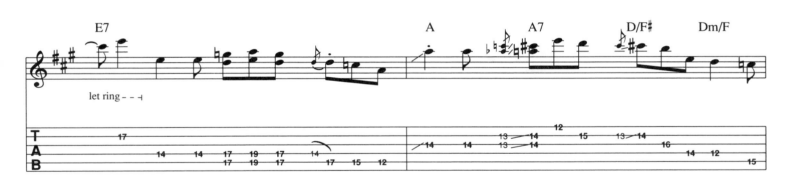

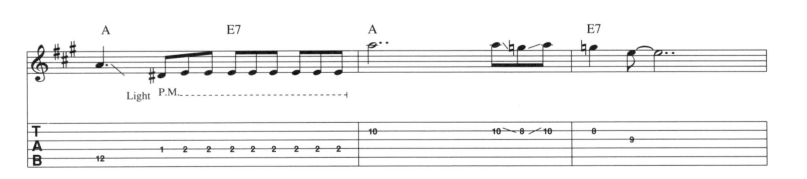

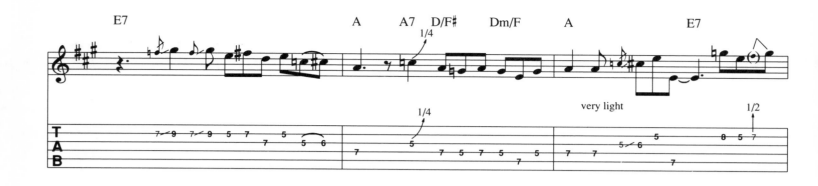

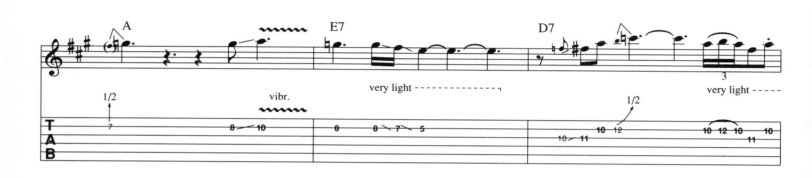

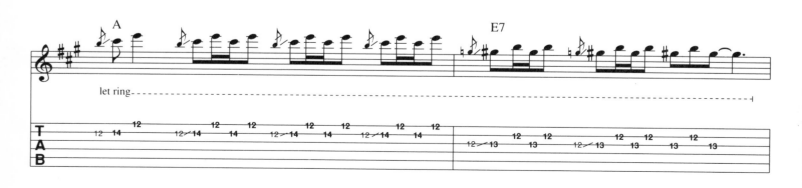

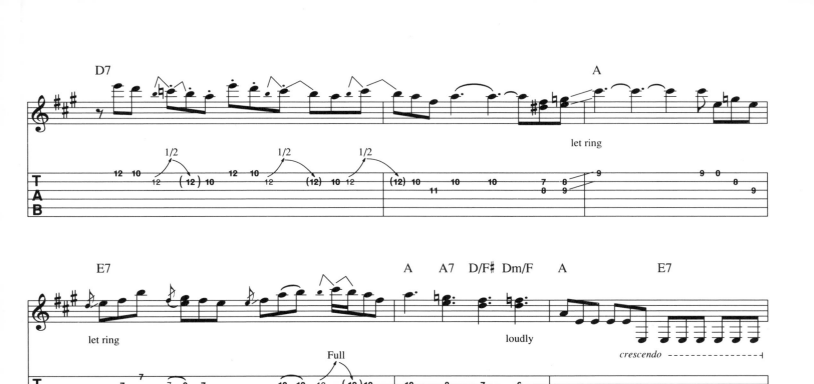

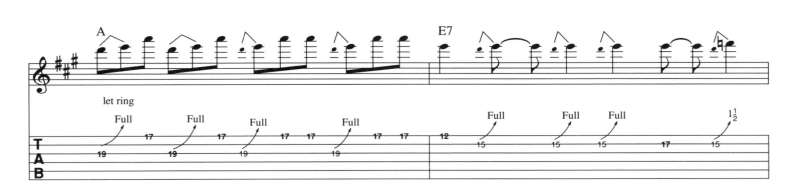

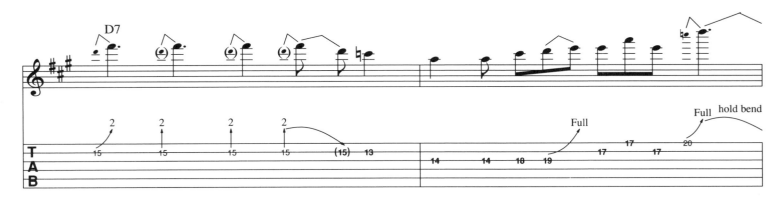

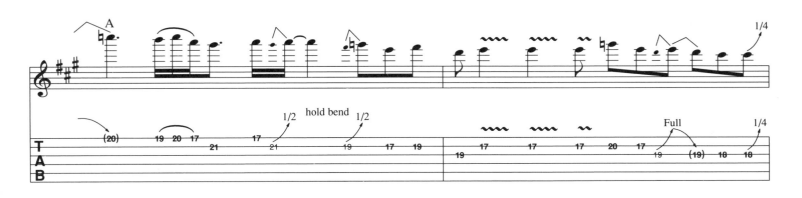

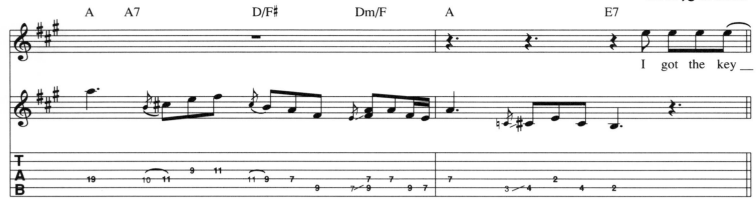

I got the key __

Instrumental

Coda

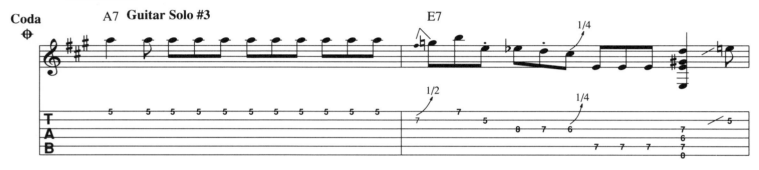

A7 **Guitar Solo #3**

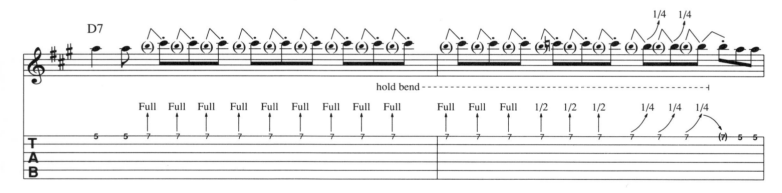

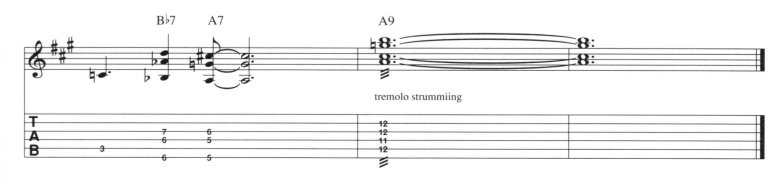

tremolo strummiing

Lonely Years.

Words & Music by John Mayall.

Slow blues shuffle

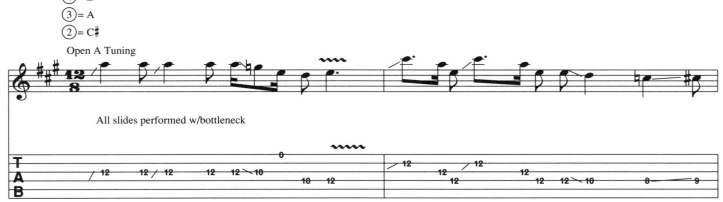

Prais - es to the wine _____   from the salt of _____ all __ my

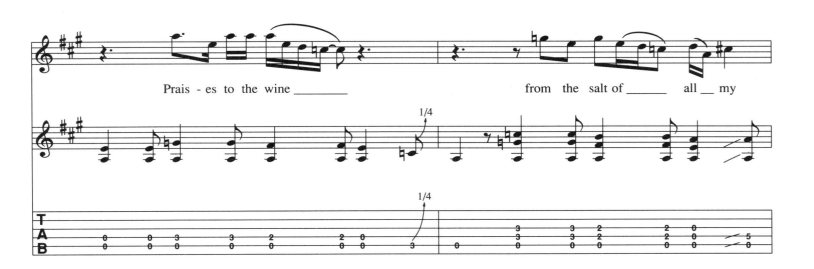

tears.

Prais - es to the wine _____ from the salt of _____ all my __

tears.

Lost ev - 'ry-thing I had, _____ I got-ta face five _____ lone - ly

I'll be meet-ing lot-ta peo- ple. ____ I got-ta start now _ and figure out my

I got-ta vis-it lot-ta peo-ple, _____ I got-ta start now _ and fig-ure out my

time. I be-lieve with a feel-in', _____

I got-ta move _____ on down the line.

42

Mean Old Frisco.

Words & Music by Arthur Crudup.

and that low down San - ta Fe.
and my pa - pa told me too.
and your cryin' won't make me stay.

Well,
Well, the

take my gal a - way,
Wom - an get in your face
more you cry, lit - tle girl.

Lord, ___ and go back out on
Son, ___ she ain't no friend to
drive me a -

to Coda ⊕

44

Slide Guitar Solo

Guitar II continues chording

46

Sleeping In The Ground.

Words & Music by Sam Myers.

Moderate blues/shuffle

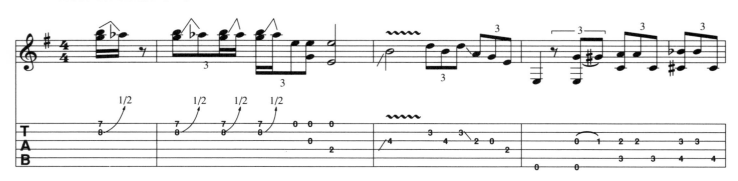

I would rath-er see you sleep-in' in the ground. _

I would ___ rath-er see you ___

sleep - in' in _____ the ground _____ than _____

to stay a-round here if you're gon-na put me down. _____

Well, I gave you all my mon-ey, ev- 'ry -

thing I o-own. Well, I gave you all my

money, ev - 'ry-thing I o - o - own. Well, some-

day I'm gon-na get luck-y, _____ and down the road you're gon-na go. ____

Snake Lake Blues.

By Eric Clapton & Bobby Whitlock.

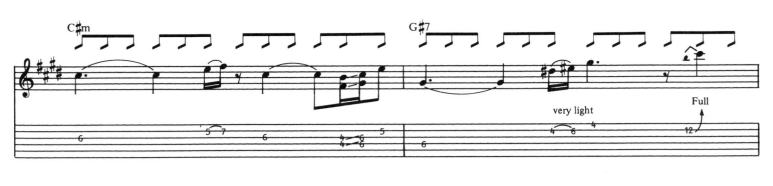

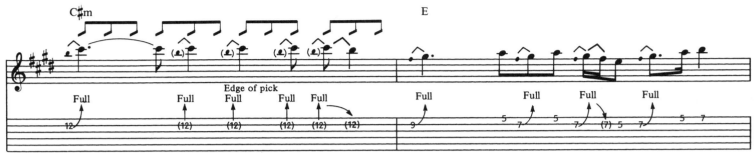

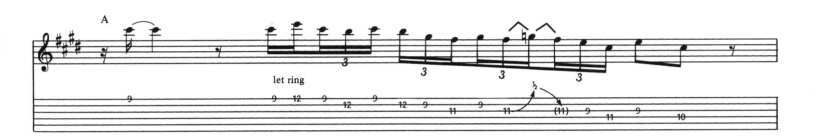

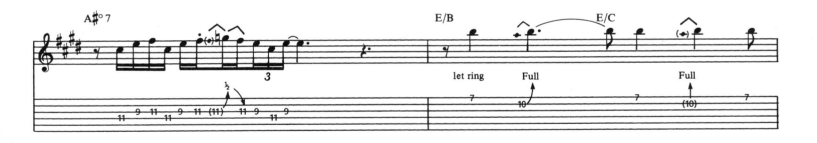

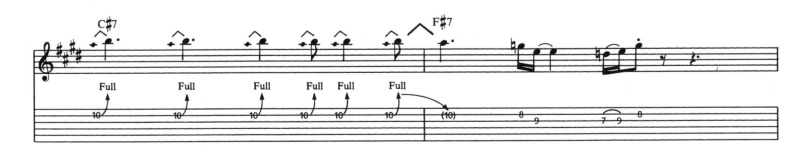

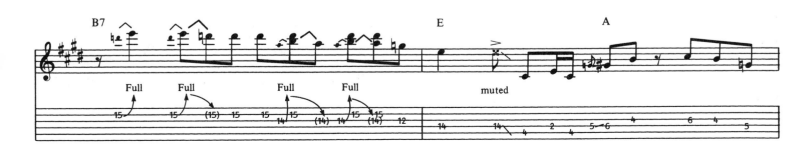

Spoonful.

Words & Music by Willie Dixon.

Moderate blues/shuffle

(Harp)

Could fill a spoon's full of dia-monds,

could fill a spoon's full of gold. ___ Just a ___ lit-tle spoon of your ___

pre-cious love _____ sat - is - fy ___ my soul. _____ Men _____

Em
___ lies _____ a - bout it; some of them cries _____ a - bout it.

Some of them dies _____ a - bout it. Ev -

- 'ry - thing's a - fight - in' a - bout the spoon - ful. ___ That spoon, that spoon, that

spoon - ful. ___ That spoon, that spoon, that spoon - ful. ___ That

spoon, that spoon, that spoon - ful. ___ That spoon, that spoon, that

spoon.

(Harp Solo)

70

4/94 (17674)